Word Perfect Spelling

BOOK ONE

BY

RONALD RIDOUT

ILLUSTRATED BY

GEORGE W. ADAMSON, M.S.I.A.

Ginn and Company Ltd

BOOKS BY THE SAME AUTHOR

Write in English, Introductory Books 1 and 2 and Books 1-8: a new style of English Workbook providing a carefully graded course on understanding, using and writing English for all 6- to 12-year olds.

Better English, Introductory Book and Books 1-5: a complete English course from about 6-12 years; illustrated in colour.

English Workbooks, Introductory Books 1 and 2 and Books 1-8: a graded course in punctuation, spelling, vocabulary, comprehension and composition. The first two are intended for infants.

English Workbooks for the Caribbean, Books 1-8: a workbook course specially written for primary schools in the Caribbean; also suitable for immigrants; illustrated in colour.

English Now, Books 1-5: a complete course in magazine form for the less academic secondary pupil; illustrated in colour.

© RONALD RIDOUT 1957
Thirty-eighth impression 1991   069107
ISBN 0 602 20985 4

Published by Ginn and Company Ltd
Prebendal House, Parson's Fee, Aylesbury, Bucks HP20 2QZ

Printed in Great Britain at the University Press, Cambridge

PREFACE

THE Introductory and eight main books of *Word Perfect Spelling* provide a systematic course in spelling and vocabulary for primary and secondary schools. Though in the first place it is correct spelling that they aim at, the books will at the same time help the pupil to gain complete mastery over the fundamental vocabulary needed by him at the various stages of his career.

Research has shown beyond dispute that the grouping of words in short lists according to common structural elements does facilitate their learning. The fact that words are held in the mind in certain patterns will, in both the short and the long run, enable them to be recalled more surely. In addition, it allows one key word to be used for unlocking many more. This, then, in the main, is the approach adopted, though other approaches have been used whenever they seemed to have a special contribution to make.

The course, however, does not end with the listing of words: it only begins there. The words have to be linked with the child's interests and brought to life by challenging activities. These activities are in themselves valuable aids to the teaching of English, but they have a vital function in improving spelling. They are based on the self-help principle whereby the pupil can hardly fail to get the right answer. This ensures that he will spell the word correctly when he writes it, and also use it correctly, so gaining the maximum benefit. For a child learns by doing, but he learns much more effectively by doing correctly.

All the patterns and more than half of the individual words used in the Introductory Book are revised in Book One. For older pupils, or for the very quick ones, *Word Perfect Spelling* will therefore provide a self-contained course if they begin with Book One. But it cannot be over-stressed that the great majority of pupils will greatly benefit from the foundation work of the Introductory Book, however rapidly they work through that book.

The work of Book One is still based entirely upon correct habit formation. Many new patterns and 455 new individual words are introduced, nearly a third of which are practised more than once. For a more detailed discussion of the uses of the books the teacher is referred to the Teachers' Manual of *Word Perfect Spelling*

A set of diagnostic tests has been added to the Teachers' Manual, thus providing the teacher with a ready means of gauging the point at which any particular child or group should join the *Word Perfect Spelling* course.

HASLEMERE, 1976   R. R.

pat

cut

hop

tug

sing

lick

fall

pay

pat	cut	lick	fall
flat	shut	kick	small
hop	tug	sing	pay
shop	jug	thing	away

You have met these words before.

Do you remember how to spell them?

Make sure you can spell them all.

Then make your own spelling lists by writing these words :

  1. For p in pat, write c, s, fl, th.
  2. For c in cut, write n, b, h, sh.
  3. For h in hop, write m, t, sh, st.
  4. For t in tug, write j, r, m, sl.
  5. For f in fall, write b, w, c, sm.
  6. For l in lick, write p, k, st, th.
  7. For s in sing, write w, r, th, br.
  8. For p in pay, write d, m, st, aw.

job	hot	sob	when	bell	spot
lot	men	far	rag	clock	spell
then	Bob	Dick	pick	jar	star
well	rock	bag	wag	frock	stick

You have met these words before, too.
How many can you still spell?

Make your own spelling lists by drawing these boxes, and putting the right words in them.

The first has been done for you.

cot	pen	sell	rob
lot			
hot			
spot			

sick	car	sock	flag

who	what	you	one
why	that	your	some
where	this	use	none
there	them	are	any

These are some more words you should know.
How many can you still spell?

Can you make these words?

1. For wh in where, write th.
2. Write n in front of one.
3. Write y in front of our.
4. Write r at the end of you.
5. For y in why, write at.

Write these words.   Put in the missing letters.

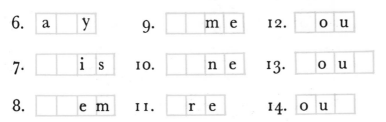

6. a ⬚ y   9. ⬚ m e   12. ⬚ o u

7. ⬚ i s   10. ⬚ n e   13. ⬚ o u

8. ⬚ e m   11. ⬚ r e   14. o u ⬚

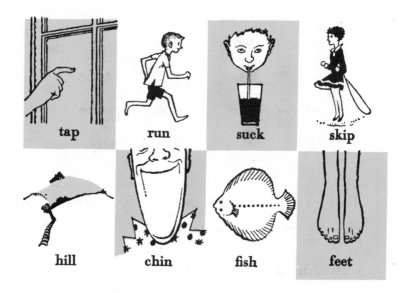

tap   run   suck   skip

hill   chin   fish   feet

Can you still spell all these words?

Make spelling lists by writing the following :

1. For t in tap, write m, c, fl, ch.
2. For r in run, write b, g, f, s.
3. For s in suck, write d, l, m, st.
4. For sk in skip, write l, d, sh, fl.
5. For h in hill, write b, k, st, sp.
6. For ch in chin, write w, t, th, sp.
7. For f in fish, write d, w, Engl.
8. For f in feet, write m, sw, sh.

feed   mend   cage

feed	mend	cage	feel
seed	bend	age	tent
weed	send	page	stage

Put the letters right in these words.

They are all in the patch. The first is <u>tent</u>.

1. | tten | 3. | endb | 5. | gea |

2. | dnse | 4. | eefl | 6. | gcae |

Write these, and put in the missing words :

7. We have to — the baby with a spoon.

8. The tent is broken. I will — it.

9. You act on a —.

10. The number of this — is 5.

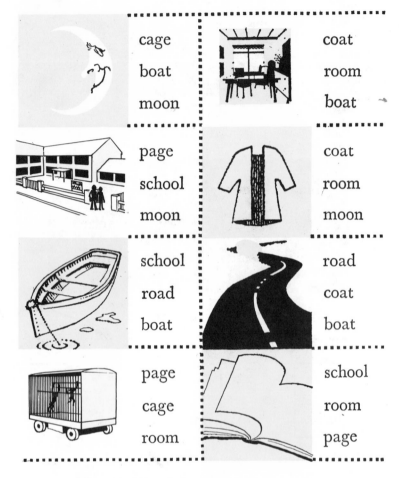

	cage		coat
	boat		room
	moon		boat
	page		coat
	school		room
	moon		moon
	school		road
	road		coat
	boat		boat
	page		school
	cage		room
	room		page

Draw the pictures.

Choose the right word for each.

Make a list of your words.

Can you spell all eight words?

1 2 3 4 5 6 7 8 9 10   20   100

one	four	seven	ten
two	five	eight	twenty
three	six	nine	hundred

Write these sentences, putting in the missing words. You will need all the words in the patch.

1. There are — days in a week.

2. Twice — are two.

3. — is one more than four.

4. Add one to two, and you get —.

5. There are — in every pair.

6. Take one away from five, and you get —.

7. Add two to seven, and you get —.

8. — is the same as half a dozen.

9. A one and two noughts stand for a —.

10. — is one less than nine.

11. Five is half of —.

12. Ten is half of —.

book	wood	moon
cook	hood	spoon
rook	food	pool

1 cook 2 3

4 5 6

8 9

Draw the pictures. Put the right word under each picture. The first one has been done for you.

Here is the alphabet, in capital and small letters:

ABCDEFGHIJKLMNOPQRSTUVWXYZ

a b c d e f g h i j k l m n o p q r s t u v w x y z

Write the twenty-six sentences below. Put in the missing words. You will find them all on page eight.

A is for ant.

B is for —.

C is for —.

D is for drum.

E is for eat.

F is for —.

G is for good.

H is for —.

I is for ice.

J is for jam.

K is for kiss.

L is for lock.

M is for —.

N is for nine.

O is for out.

P is for —.

Q is for quick.

R is for —.

S is for —.

T is for took.

U is for use.

V is for vest.

W is for —.

X is for x in box.

Y is for yes.

Z is for zip.

bud   neck   sleep

bud	neck	keep	been
mud	peck	sleep	desk
stud	speck	peep	plum

1. Instead of b in <u>bud</u>, write m, d, st.
2. Instead of n in <u>neck</u>, write d, p, sp, ch.
3. Instead of p in <u>peep</u>, write k, sl, d, w.
4. Instead of b in <u>been</u>, write s, k, gr, qu.
5. Instead of s in <u>sum</u>, write h, g, pl, ch.

S	L	E	E	P		D		
P		A		E		B	O	O	K
E		T	O	E		E			I
C				P	E	E	L		C
K	E	E	N			N	E	C	K

How many words can you find in this puzzle? There are twelve. Make a list of them.

bull   cow   nest

bull	**cow**	**nest**	**put**
pull	**how**	**best**	**chest**
full	**now**	**vest**	**down**

If you add s to nest, it means more than one : nest—nests.

Now write these words so that they will mean more than one :

    1. bull   2. cow   3. vest   4. chest

5. I am the father of a calf. Write my name.
6. I am the mother of a calf. Write mine too.

 . Put the letters right in these words :

7. | lluf | 8. | owdn | 9. | ohw | 10. | onw |

cow   mouse   horse

goat   kitten lion

sheep   fox   tiger

We say that <u>cat</u> rhymes with <u>hat</u>.
Write the words that rhyme with :
  1. coat   2. how   3. keep   4. box

Write these, putting in the missing words :
4. The — gives us milk.
5. The — gives us wool.
6. A — is like a rat, but smaller.
7. A — is a baby cat.
8. In the picture, the — is just below the horse.

toss	my	ever	sky
moss	fly	every	clever
cross	dry	never	across

Can you write these words, putting in the missing letters ? All the words are in the patch.

1. `d` `y`   Not at all wet.

2. `y`   To move in the air.

3. `y`   What you can see up in the air.

4. `.` `s` `s`   To throw.

5. `o`   Very low, soft, green plant.

6. `e` `r`   Very good at doing things.

7. `y`   All.

8. `s` `s`   From one side to the other.

9. `e` `r`   At no time.

10. `s` `s`   Bad tempered.

kind	was	only	cry
find	want	over	were
blind	wash	very	said

Draw a ladder with six steps like this.
ı u. these words on the right steps.

1. the word only		6
2. the word beginning with f		5
3. the word that ends with er		4
4. the word that has ant in it		3
5. the word that has aid in it		2
6. the word meaning he cannot see	only	1

Write these words. Put the letters right.

7.   s h w a   to make yourself clean

8.   y c r   to weep

9.   l i d n b   cannot see

10.   n d k i   nice and helpful

Let's make sure.

(1)	sky	sheep	goat	food
	dry	sheet	road	room
	why	green	three	school

(2)	neck	plum	seven	ever
	vest	stud	eight	never
	desk	stuck	nine	clever

(3)	sing	stick	here	ten
	thing	luck	where	twenty
	thick	clock	there	tent

Copy this carefully :
Dick was kind to the blind man.
He took him by the arm
and led him across the road.
That is the kind of help
that a blind man wants.

Sunday	come
Monday	some
Tuesday	before
Wednesday	after
Thursday	little
Friday	middle
Saturday	week

Write these, putting in the missing words :

1. Monday comes just before —.

2. — comes just before Thursday.

3. Saturday comes just after —.

4. — comes just after Tuesday.

5. Tuesday comes just before —.

6. Thursday comes just after —.

7. — is the middle day of the week.

Suppose the week went backwards :

8. Write the days in the order in which they would then come.

bit – bite	line	ride
hid – hide	fine	kite
win – wine	nine	wife

W	**N**	**E**
F		

1. Copy this puzzle.
Write in the letters to make four words from the spelling list above.

Can you make these words?

2. After wi– write ne, fe, de, pe, se.

3. After ri– write de, pe, ce, se.

4. After fi– write ne, ve, re.

Write these words with the letters in the right places :

5. | i h d | 7. | n w i | 9. | e i t b |

6. | e i h d | 8. | e n w i | 10. | f w e i |

summer	list	wing	ding-dong
butter	sister	thing	song
supper	winter	spring	long

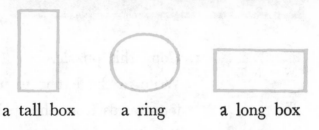

a tall box   a ring   a long box

1. Draw a tall box. Write in it all the words that end in –er.

2. Draw a ring. Write in it the three words that end in –ing.

3. Draw a long box. Write in it the two words that begin with su–.

4. Draw a ring. Write in it the two words that begin with l.

5. Draw a tall box. Write in it the five words that begin with s.

6. Draw a long box. Write in it the three words that end in –ong.

hat — hate   game   late

Sam — same   came   make

fad — fade   name   made

S	A	M	E
A		A	
F	A	D	E
E		E	

M	A	T	E
I		A	
N	A	M	E
E		E	

T	A	L	E
I		A	
M	A	K	E
E		E	

1. Write all the words you can find in the puzzles. There are twelve altogether.

2. For n in name, write g, c, s, t, bl.

3. For m in make, write c, b, l, aw.

4. Make four new words by writing e at the end of tap, can, mad, pip.

5. After ca– write ke, ne, se, me, ve.

6. For h in hide, write w, r, s, t, sl.

7. For m in mine, write f, l, n, w, p, sh, tw.

Mike has two sisters.
Their names are Kate and Jane.
They all like to go to the sea-side.
Mike likes to ride his bike on the sand.
Kate likes to dive under the waves.
Jane likes to make cakes with the wet sand.

Jane	name	like	dive
make	wave	bike	under
cake	their	ride	sister

Copy the sentences about Mike and his sisters.
Put a line under all the words from the patch.

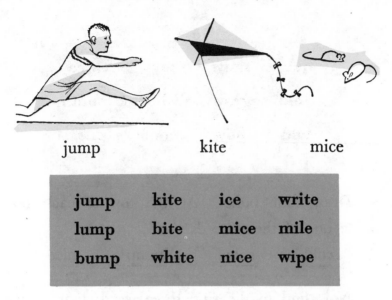

jump   kite   mice

jump	kite	ice	write
lump	bite	mice	mile
bump	white	nice	wipe

Find the missing letters.   Write the words.

1. | b | | | e | You do this with your teeth.

2. | w | | | | e | You do this with a pencil.

3. | | | | p | You do this with your legs.

4. | | | p | | You can do this with a rag.

5. | | | t | | This flies in the air.

6. | | h | | | This is a colour.

7. | | | | This is very cold.

8. | | | | | This means more than one mouse.

9. | | | | | Add n to ice, and you get this.

10. | | | | | For l in lump, write b.

old	snow	love	twice
cold	grow	above	pump
fold	show	come	pile

Draw four boxes. At the top of each box write one of these words :

cold   snow   bump   nice

Now find in the ring three words that rhyme with cold.   Write them in the first box.

Do the same with the other boxes.

mice	sold	blow
bold	rice	lump
grow	slow	fold
jump	twice	pump

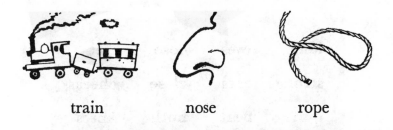

train   nose   rope

pain	again	nose	rope
rain	aid	rose	hope
train	wait	close	poke

Put the letters right in these words :

1. a n r i   It falls from the clouds.
2. i d a   Help.
3. s e n o   Part of your face.
4. o s e c l   To shut.
5. n t r a i   It runs on rails.
6. n a i g a   Once more.
7. o s e r   A flower.
8. e p o r   Thick string.
9. t w a i   To stay till someone comes.
10. a i p n   What you feel when you are hurt.

long	eyes	nose	feet
strong	ears	close	cheeks
quite	neat	both	knees

Two little eyes that open and close,
Two little ears and one little nose,
Two little lips and one little chin,
And two little cheeks with a nose shut in.

Two little arms both round and neat,
Two little legs and two little feet,
Two little knees quite hard and strong,
And two little hands never still very long.

1. Can you say this poem? Write it out.
Put a line under all the words from the patch.

2. Now write in capital letters all the words
under which you have put a line.

3. Write these words so that they will mean
one only: eyes, ears, cheeks, hands, knees.

HOW TO LEARN TO SPELL

1	Look at the word. Say it softly.
2	Look at the word. Say the letters.
3	Close your eyes. Say the letters.
4	Look at the word to see if you have spelt it right.
5	Write the word. See if you spelt it right.

ink	drink	out	loud
pink	wind	about	gold
sink	hint	shout	nail

1. I blow the leaves about. Write my name.
2. You hit me with a hammer. Write my name.
3. I help the pen to write. Write my name.
4. I am a loud call. Write my name.
5. I am water, tea or milk. Write my name.

live	wave	talk	milk
give	face	walk	mouse
gave	race	chalk	house

Write the words that rhyme with :

1. gave   2. race   3. house   4. live

5. How many of the words in the patch can you write with these letters? Try to find eight.

a   c   e   f   g   h   i   k   l   t   v   w

6. Instead of w in <u>wave</u>, write g, c, s, h.
7. Instead of r in <u>race</u>, write f, l, p, pl.
8. Instead of w in <u>walk</u>, write t, ch.
9. Instead of m in <u>mouse</u>, write h.

other	father	aunt	call
mother	sister	uncle	called
brother	Mary	John	David

1. Put m in front of other. Then put br.
2. I begin with a capital D. Write my name.
3. I begin with a small s. Write my name.
4. Put fat in front of her !

Copy this. Put a line under all the words from the patch.

I have two brothers.
One brother is called John.
The other is called David.
My mother has one brother.
We call him Uncle Tom.
My father has one sister.
We call her Aunt Mary.

bird   round   mouth

girl	first	sound	place
bird	round	count	joke
third	ground	mouth	home

Put the letters right in these words :

1. | b d i r | This flies in the air.
2. | o u n r d | A ball is this shape.
3. | o u m t h | You put food in this to eat.
4. | o u n g r d | You walk on this.
5. | i r t h d | This comes after the second.
6. | i r f t s | This comes before the second.
7. | o e k j | This is very funny.
8. | o u d n s | This is a noise.
9. | e m o h | Your own house is this.
10. | i r g l | She will be a woman when she grows up.

Let's make sure.

(4)

weed	time	train	cold
cheek	mile	wait	gold
knee	twice	tail	talk

(5)

round	wave	mother	race
shout	cake	brother	place
loud	late	father	plate

(6)

rope	strong	ground	wipe
poke	thing	count	quite
close	Tuesday	mouth	write

Copy this carefully :

I ride to school on my bike.
The school is a mile
from our house.
We have a nice time there.
I never like staying away.

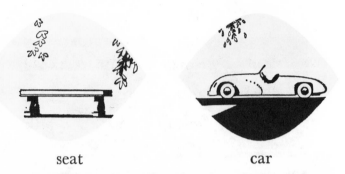

seat car

sea	**read**	**car**	**pound**
eat	**mean**	**cart**	**mind**
seat	**cheap**	**start**	**pint**

Write these, putting in the missing words :

1. If you put s in front of eat, you get —.
2. If you put t after sea, you get —.
3. If you put t after —, you get cart.
4. If you take c away from —, you get art.

Can you make these words ?

5. For s in seat, write b, m, n, h.
6. For c in cart, write t, st, d.
7. For m in mind, write f, w, k, bl.
8. For p in pound, write s, gr, r, f.

buns	egg	cakes	peas
butter	fish	flakes	beans
pudding	jam	food	meat

Write these sentences. Put in the missing letters.

1. P – – – and b – – n – grow in the garden.
2. Jim likes – – sh and chips.
3. You eat your – – dd – – – after the – ea –.
4. B – – – er is nice on – – n –.
5. You put – – m on bread and – – tt – –.
6. You put milk on corn – – – – es.
7. The baker sells – u – – and – – k – –.
8. The hen has laid an – – –.
9. All these things are good – oo –.

10. Make new words by adding s to these :
    bun   egg   cake   pea   bean   pudding
11. For f in <u>food,</u> write g, h, w, st, bl.

arm   dart   chair

arm	dart	hair	chair
farm	lark	fair	pair
hard	barn	fairy	dark

Add a letter. (Add h to air and you get hair.)

1. Make air into what grows on your head.

2. Make hair into something you sit on.

3. Make arm into a place where you find cows.

4. Make art into something you throw.

5. Make ark into a kind of bird.

Make these words mean more than one :

6. arm   7. farm   8. chair   9. barn

10. Write the word that rhymes with card.

11. Write the word that rhymes with part.

to hear   to read

much	ear	each	card
such	hear	reach	found
rich	near	read	heap

Put in the missing words :

1. Take n from <u>near</u>, and you get —.
2. Take r from <u>reach</u>, and you get —.
3. Add h to <u>ear</u>, and you get —.
4. Take c from <u>cheap</u>, and you get —.
5. Write s for m in <u>much</u>, and you get —.
6. Write c for h in <u>hard</u>, and you get —.
7. Write f for s in <u>sound</u>, and you get —.
8. Write r for l in <u>lead</u>, and you get —.
9. You — with your ears.
10. A — man has — money.

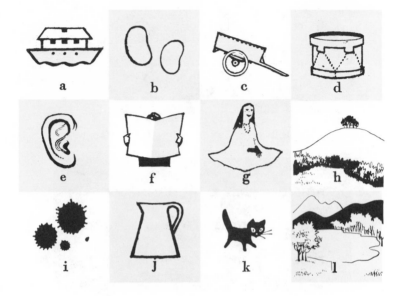

Make a picture A B C. Draw the pictures, and put the right words under them.

Can you spell all the words?

Can you make another picture A B C with your own words?

ear	beans	cart	hill
ark	girl	father	drum
jug	ink	kitten	lake

m n o p

q r s t

u v w x

y z

Do the same with this page.

queen	mouth	train	seat
zip	nest	rope	umbrella
vest	plate	yacht	Xmas-tree
	owl	wall	

miss	more	most	past
kiss	sore	post	fast
less	store	lost	last

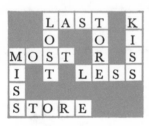

1. Write all the words that you can find in this puzzle. There are eight.

2. Write the word that rhymes with <u>mess</u>.

3. Write the word that rhymes with <u>kiss</u>.

4. Write two words that rhyme with <u>sore</u>.

5. Write three words that rhyme with <u>mast</u>.

6. For l in <u>last,</u> write f, p, m.

7. For m in <u>more,</u> write s, c, st.

8. For l in <u>lost,</u> write c, fr.

9. For l in <u>less,</u> write m, dr, pr, bl, gu, unl, expr.

10. After <u>post,</u> write s, ed, ing, er, age.

thick	thin	cold	hot
big	small	dry	wet
tall	short	long	short
fast	slow	ill	well

Thick is the opposite of thin.
Big is the opposite of small.
Dry is the opposite of wet.   thick   thin

Can you find the opposites of the words below?
Do the box on the left first.   Begin like this :
1. strong   weak
2. small

1. strong	short	7. wet	little
2. small	fast	8. white	open
3. long	bad	9. first	slow
4. thin	weak	10. shut	dry
5. slow	thick	11. big	black
6. good	big	12. quick	last

look	looking	pull	pulling
cook	cooking	push	pushing
talk	talking	eat	eating
walk	walking	speak	speaking

The word talking comes from the word talk.
Write the words that these come from :

1. looking
2. speaking
3. reading
4. teaching
5. raining
6. painting
7. snowing
8. blowing
9. jumping

Add -ing to these words :

10. walk
11. push
12. fall
13. teach
14. eat
15. kiss
16. start
17. count

18. Copy this carefully :
   Outside, the rain was falling fast.
   Inside, Mary was reading her book.
   Her brother John was painting.

1. armchair	7. inside
2. birthday	8. outside
3. blackbird	9. postman
4. bedroom	10. milkman
5. cannot	11. grandmother
6. football	12. grandfather

Each word is made up of two small words.

Copy the lists. Take out the small words and put them in boxes. Begin like this :

1. armchair   [arm]   [chair]

2. birthday   [   ]   [   ]

Copy this carefully :

The blackbird was singing outside in the tree.

Bob was singing inside
in his bedroom.
It was his birthday.
His grandfather
gave him a football.
Bob was very happy.

happy	funny	penny	little
Daddy	sunny	lesson	apple
Mummy	sorry	letter	sitting

Find the missing letters. Write the words.

1. M _ m m _ _   A way of saying mother.

2. _ _ d d _ _   A way of saying father.

3. _ _ t t _ _   Small.

4. _ p p _ _   It grows on a tree.

5. _ _ n n _   It is this when the sun shines.

6. _ _ s s _ _   Something to learn.

7. _ _ t t _ _   There are four in THIS.

8. _ _ n n _   A pound has 100 of them.

9. _ _ p p _   This is the opposite of sad.

10. _ _ n n _   Jokes are this.

11. _ _ t t _ _ _   Comes from the word <u>sit</u>.

12. _ _ r r _   You say this when you have done something wrong.

stop	wind	when	blue
stand	hill	where	sheep
still	away	white	blow

You have met most of these words before.

Can you spell them all ?

Can you learn the poem and write it out ?

White sheep, white sheep
   On a blue hill.
When the wind stops
   You all stand still.
You all run away
   When the wind blows.
White sheep, white sheep,
   Where do you go ?

sit	sitting	ride	riding
skip	skipping	write	writing
swim	swimming	dive	diving
run	running	slide	sliding

1 Mary   2 John   3 Richard   4 Pam

5 Jill   6 David   7 Peter   8 Susan

Write a sentence saying what each child is doing.
Begin like this :

    1. Mary is skipping.

    2. John is

Let's make sure.

(7)

wise	blow	more	mouth
shine	grow	store	ground
quite	throw	shore	count

(8)

speaking	girl	green	eating
reading	bird	queen	talking
teaching	first	sweep	pushing

(9)

diving	happy	cannot	running
riding	funny	inside	sitting
writing	penny	outside	putting

Copy this carefully :

Three girls are all doing something.

Mary is sweeping the room.

Pat is writing a letter,

and Jill is reading her book.

For extra work

(1)
bake	clean	lane	class
snake	cheat	shame	grass
shake	cream	lace	dress

(2)
have	home	stopping	price
having	stone	stepping	drive
loving	note	patting	smile

(3)
think	work	able	once
drink	brush	table	dance
thank	stool	woman	fence

(4)
pride	water	paper	letter
slide	splash	baby	word
stride	cloud	lady	sentence